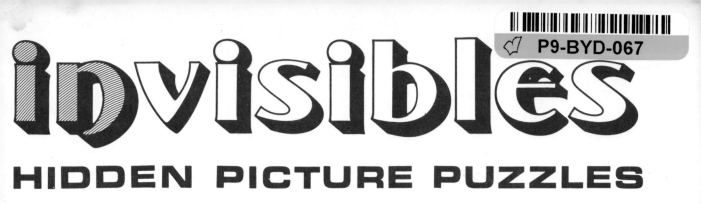

invisibles

HIDDEN PICTURE PUZZLES

WRITTEN AND ILLUSTRATED BY

Larry Evans

STARSTREAM PRODUCTS
WINSTON-SALEM, NORTH CAROLINA

IN-VISIBLE 1

ROOTS

Grandpa is trying to find out just who his ancestors were. One of them is there in the picture with him. Grandpa's favorite saying is, "Well, I'll be a monkey's uncle".

STARSTREAM PRODUCTS EDITION

This special edition created by permission of Troubadour Press.

ISBN: 0-912300-84-1

Solutions are in the back of the book.

1 2 3 4 5 6 7 8 9 10   January 1980

Starstream Products
P.O. Box 2222
Winston-Salem, N.C. 27102

IN-VISIBLE 2

PIRATE CHASE

The square rigged clipper ship is outrunning the pirate ship by using all her sails. Hidden on board are an anchor, a ship's wheel, oar, dinghy, telescope, pirate sword *and* a rotten old pirate.

IN-VISIBLE 3

GIANT'S CASTLE

This magnificent castle belongs to a giant named Ralph. He doesn't like visitors so he is hiding. If *you* can find him, ask him how the weather is up there. He will think that is funny and give you a *big hug*.

IN-VISIBLE 4

THE FOXY FOX

The fox from the cover of this book is being chased by a horse and rider and three hounds. The fox thinks he's really clever, but they're *all* right there in the picture with him. I think this fox has his goose cooked!

IN-VISIBLE 5

A HOT SUMMER DAY

All the people have gone to the beach and left the cat home. Just in case she gets lonely the hired hand from IN-VISIBLE 17 is there on a *surfboard* along with two girls in bathing suits, a sailboat and a guitar.

IN-VISIBLE 6

LIGHTHOUSE

A wide variety of boats and ships have found their way upon this rocky shore. A Roman Trireme with its sails and oars, a Mississippi River boat, a Chinese Junk, an Ocean Liner and a Venetian Gondola. See if you can find them all.

IN-VISIBLE 7

CHECKERS

Uncle Jake and his friend Wilbur are retired, but the tools of their trade are there in the old country store with them. A saw, hammer, hatchet, pickaxe, screwdriver, and scissors are somewhere in the picture. They both were building contractors. The scissors were for cutting *red tape*.

IN-VISIBLE 8

STILL LIFE

The vase of flowers is ready for the artist to
paint, but he is no where to be found. Find a
paint brush, palette *and* the artist before the
flowers wilt.

IN-VISIBLE 9
THE QUEEN

Her Royal Majesty is ready for the official portrait to be painted by our elusive artist from the last IN-VISIBLE. She wants her faithful dog to be in the painting but he is off chasing a rabbit. Find the rabbit, the dog, a hairbrush and the King somewhere in the picture.

IN-VISIBLE 10
THE HIDDEN JUNGLE

On pages 20 and 21 lies an illustration of the jungle watering hole. The Abongo natives *know* that the animals come here to drink, and the two tribesmen have been waiting for three days to capture an animal. The snake has been waiting three days for the *natives* to cross the old log. Hidden for the last three days right there in the picture are an elephant, rhino, giraffe, monkey, zebra, alligator, lion and antelope. See if you can find the animals *before* the natives capture them.

IN-VISIBLE 11

PREHISTORIC WALK

The hikers are taking a path that leads right into the age of Dinosaurs. Find the Brontosaurus, Pteranodon (flying Dinosaur) and the ferocious Tyrannosaurus Rex.

IN-VISIBLE 12

INDIAN HUNTER

The pioneers have driven all the animals into hiding. Running Bear is searching for a buffalo, big-horned sheep, beaver and a moose. They are all there in the picture with him along with the pioneer hunter who scared them away with his gun.

IN-VISIBLE 13

DAYDREAM

Mary Jane is daydreaming about the circus. She doesn't realize that the circus is right there in the picture with her. Find the elephant, lion, trapeze artist (on the trapeze), cotton candy, tightrope walker (on the tightrope, naturally), and three clowns. (No you silly, her clown doll doesn't count.)

IN-VISIBLE 14

THE BIRDS

Sally Ann swings in the giant sycamore tree every afternoon. When she swings all the birds disappear. Find eleven birds in the picture including an owl, a flamingo and a toucan. There is also a vulture, an egret, a gull, an eagle, a *tiny* duck, two birds trying to fly away and one bird just sitting there.

IN-VISIBLE 15

BLACKSMITH SHOP

In 1899, the blacksmith was the most important man in town. He shoed horses and fixed wagon wheels. Find in the picture with him, three objects that helped make the blacksmith obsolete: a steam locomotive, a horseless carriage and an early airplane.

IN-VISIBLE 16

HAUNTED HOUSE

Nancy and her sister Elizabeth thought they would explore the old abandoned house on a warm summer's night. Suddenly lights appeared upstairs and weird noises echoed through the house. You see, the house is *really* haunted. Find the skull, owl, bat, ghost, spider, black cat and the old witch hidden in the picture.

IN-VISIBLE 17

THE BARN DOOR

The farmer and his wife have found the door to the barn open. The pig, mule and rooster have vanished. Also missing are the tractor, shovel and hoe. The hired hand who left the barn door open is also gone, but he may be found in IN-VISIBLE #5 on a surfboard.

IN-VISIBLE 18

GONE FISHING

It's a perfect day for fishing. Bobby is playing hooky again. He's not going to catch anything even though at least twenty fish are there in the picture with him. There is also a whale, octopus and sea horse. Bobby's going to catch something else when he gets home.

SOLUTIONS

1

2

3

4

5

6

7

8

9

10

11

12

13

14

15

16

17

18

FRONT COVER

BACK COVER